Verbal Reasoning: Vocabulary

Multiple Choice Practice Tests BOOK 2

How to use this book to make the most of 11 plus exam preparation

It is important to remember that for 11 plus exams there is no national syllabus, no pass mark and no retake option! It is therefore vitally important that your child is fully primed in order to perform to the best of their ability to give themselves the best possible chance on the day.

CEM Verbal Reasoning Tests

CEM Verbal Reasoning Tests consists of short timed tests with a mixture of verbal reasoning questions. Logic, vocabulary and time management skills are assessed with these practice tests.

Never has it been more useful to learn from mistakes!

Students can improve by as much as 15 percent, not only by focused practice but also by targeting any weak areas.

How to manage your child's own practice

To get the most up-to-date information, visit our website, www.elevenplusexams.co.uk, the largest UK online resource with over 65,000 webpages and a forum administered by a select group of experienced moderators.

About the authors

The Eleven Plus Exams **First Past the Post®** series has been created by a team of experienced tutors and authors from leading British universities.

Published by University of Buckingham Press.

With special thanks to the children who tested our material at the Eleven Plus Exams centre in Harrow.

Please note the UBP is not associated with CEM or The University of Durham in any way. This book does not include any official questions and it is not endorsed by CEM or The University of Durham.

CEM, Centre for Evaluation and Monitoring, Durham University and *The University of Durham* are all trademarks of The University of Durham.

ISBN: 9781908684783

About Us

ElevenPlusExams is the UK's largest website offering a vast amount of information and advice, a moderated online forum, books, downloadable materials and online services to enhance your child's chances of success in the demanding selective schools entrance exams, namely the 11+ and common entrance exams.

The company also provides specialist 11+ tuition and is a supplier of online services to schools.

ElevenPlusExams is recognised as a trusted and authoritative source of information and advice. It has been quoted in numerous national newspapers (including The Telegraph, The Sunday Observer, The Daily Mail, The Sunday Telegraph), BBC Radio and national television (BBC1 and Channel 4).

Set up in 2004, the website grew from an initial 20 webpages to more than 65,000 today and has been visited by millions of parents.

The website gives parents impartial advice on preparation, techniques, 11+ exams in their area and preparation material based on actual experience. The forum is the largest for 11+ in the UK, and is moderated by over 20 experts including parents, experienced tutors and authors who collectively provide support both before the exams, and for those parents who are also unfortunate enough to have to appeal the decisions.

Visit our website to benefit from the wealth of information and advice and see why we are the market's leading 'one-stop-shop' for all your eleven plus needs.

✓ Comprehensive quality content and advice written by 11+ experts

✓ 11+ Online Shop supplying a wide range of practice books, e-papers, software and apps

✓ UK's largest online 11+ Forum moderated by experts

✓ Lots of FREE practice papers to download

✓ Professional tuition services optimising state of the art technology

✓ Short Revision courses

✓ Year long 11+ courses

✓ Mock exams tailored to mirror those of the main examining bodies

Other titles in the First Past The Post® Series

11 + Essentials CEM Style Practice Tests

Verbal Reasoning: Cloze Tests
Book 1
9781908684288

Verbal Reasoning: Cloze Tests
Book 2
9781908684356

Verbal Reasoning: Grammar and
Spelling Multiple Choice Books 1 & 2
9781908684646 | 9781908684790

Verbal Reasoning: Vocabulary
Multiple Choice Books 1 & 2
9781908684639 | 9781908684783

Numerical Reasoning: Multi-part
Books 1 & 2
9781908684301 | 9781908684363

Numerical Reasoning: Multi-part
(Multiple Choice) Books 1 & 2
9781908684769 | 9781908684776
NEW for 2016

Numerical Reasoning: Quick-fire
Books 1 & 2
9781908684431 | 9781908684448

Numerical Reasoning: Quick-fire
(Multiple Choice) Books 1 & 2
9781908684653 | 9781908684752
NEW for 2016

English: Comprehensions
Book 1
9781908684295

English: Comprehensions
Book 2
9781908684486

3D Non-Verbal Reasoning
Book 1
9781908684318

3D Non-Verbal Reasoning
Book 2
9781908684479

Mental Arithmetic
Book 1
9781908684462

Numerical Reasoning:
Worded Problems
Book 1
9781908684806
NEW for 2016

Maths Dictionary
9781908684493

NEW for 2016

11 + Practice Paper Packs

Non-Verbal Reasoning
Practice Papers
9781908684134

English
Practice Papers
9781908684103

Verbal Reasoning
Practice Papers
9781908684127

Mathematics
Practice Papers
9781908684110

Contents

Each practice test has a timer that indicates the recommended time within which you should complete the test.

x minutes

BLANK PAGE

FIRST PAST THE POST®

Synonyms

Marking Grid: Test 1																				
Question	1	2	3	4	5	6	7	8	9	10	11	12	13	14	15	16	17	18	19	20	Total
✓ ✗																					/20

Marking Grid: Test 2																				
Question	1	2	3	4	5	6	7	8	9	10	11	12	13	14	15	16	17	18	19	20	Total
✓ ✗																					/20

Marking Grid: Test 3																				
Question	1	2	3	4	5	6	7	8	9	10	11	12	13	14	15	16	17	18	19	20	Total
✓ ✗																					/20

Test 1 - Synonyms: Similar Words

4 minutes

Choose one word out of the three options that means the same or nearly the same as the word on the left.

Example Word	A	B	C
breach	honour	admire	contravene

	Word	A	B	C
1	equivalent	opposite	counterpart	peculiar
2	desperate	craving	ambivalent	interested
3	abscond	remain	escape	secure
4	smoulder	fear	extinguish	burn
5	forcible	violent	gentle	restrained
6	preference	forgotten	favourite	wondrous
7	transfer	stir	still	shift
8	amateur	expert	non-professional	elite
9	conscience	principles	imagination	hate
10	disastrous	beloved	cataclysmic	wonderful

		A	**B**	**C**
11	**prejudice**	disapproval	love	bias
12	**erosion**	destruction	fragility	terrain
13	**bemused**	amused	content	puzzled
14	**burden**	wanted	convenience	cargo
15	**clamorous**	loud	quiet	busy
16	**hassle**	placid	annoyance	depression
17	**criticism**	condemnation	ignorance	grudge
18	**precipitous**	gradual	steep	low
19	**abduct**	invite	seize	receive
20	**bliss**	anger	uncertain	happiness

Test 2 - Synonyms: Similar Words

5 minutes

Choose one word out of the four options that means the same or nearly the same as the word on the left.

Example Word	A	Ⓑ	C	D
antipathetic	love	hostile	confused	sympathetic

	Word	A	B	C	D
1	nutritious	family	rare	healthy	unhealthy
2	orientate	travel	diminish	separate	align
3	spectacle	display	normality	lock	invitation
4	unite	negative	amalgamate	disperse	break
5	sodden	vulnerable	layered	uncomfortable	soaked
6	prepared	assembled	wary	reluctant	unprepared
7	pure	experienced	contaminated	pleasant	unblended
8	retentive	inattentive	absorbent	waterproof	forgetful
9	secure	precarious	naïve	fastened	unsettled
10	opportune	disadvantageous	subtle	discerning	favourable

		A	B	C	D
11	**tactful**	authoritative	casual	discreet	awkward
12	**upstanding**	parallel	whole	absent	respectable
13	**terminate**	continue	begin	surprise	cease
14	**acquaint**	polite	unfamiliar	familiarize	ignore
15	**console**	compete	comfort	distress	perplex
16	**contest**	dispute	commend	agree	enquire
17	**worthy**	virtuous	superfluous	disreputable	renowned
18	**reckless**	prudent	rash	calculated	suppressed
19	**hospitable**	hostile	odious	petulant	gracious
20	**remote**	close	lengthy	distant	proximity

Test 3 - Synonyms: Similar Words

6 minutes

Choose one word out of the five options that means the same or nearly the same as the word on the left.

Example Word	A	B	Ⓒ	D	E
dangle	passive	evolve	suspend	pensive	loath

	Word	A	B	C	D	E
1	supple	thin	distorted	unique	flawless	flexible
2	exclusive	vague	special	inclusive	reoccurring	incomplete
3	mediocre	inadequate	exaggerated	average	substandard	superior
4	corrupt	peculiar	immoral	conservative	honest	optimistic
5	whim	morality	cry	impulse	rotate	deduce
6	wretched	unhappy	moral	dishonourable	passionate	comfortable
7	forecast	hindsight	casting	conclude	highlight	predict
8	foster	nurture	suppress	neglect	monitor	fragment
9	contaminate	sterilise	pollute	disinfect	cleanse	sterilize
10	beneficiary	guard	opposition	heir	referee	mediator

		A	B	C	D	E
11	**betrayal**	treachery	loyalty	faithfulness	fealty	bon
12	**mystify**	enlighten	dumbfound	advise	bewilder	inform
13	**pungent**	bitter	tasty	delicious	quenching	thirsty
14	**pretence**	thorough	disguise	genuine	hunger	edition
15	**collide**	crash	connection	collate	create	confer
16	**cunning**	stupid	open	wily	sincere	blunt
17	**orderly**	messy	attempt	smart	daring	dated
18	**demure**	bold	cautious	frightened	aggressive	reserved
19	**needful**	unusual	reliant	independent	maverick	bold
20	**enable**	allow	regard	emulate	prevent	imitate

BLANK PAGE

FIRST PAST THE POST®

Antonyms

Marking Grid: Test 4																				
Question	1	2	3	4	5	6	7	8	9	10	11	12	13	14	15	16	17	18	19	20	Total
✓ ✗																					/20

Marking Grid: Test 5																				
Question	1	2	3	4	5	6	7	8	9	10	11	12	13	14	15	16	17	18	19	20	Total
✓ ✗																					/20

Marking Grid: Test 6																				
Question	1	2	3	4	5	6	7	8	9	10	11	12	13	14	15	16	17	18	19	20	Total
																					/20

Marking Grid: Test 7																				
Question	1	2	3	4	5	6	7	8	9	10	11	12	13	14	15	16	17	18	19	20	Total
✓ ✗																					/20

Test 4 - Antonyms: Opposite Words

4 minutes

Choose one word out of the three options that means the opposite or nearly the opposite to the word on the left.

Example			
Word	A	B	**C**
sociable	companionable	funny	shy

	Word	A	B	C
1	**animosity**	rancour	goodwill	antipathy
2	**faithful**	dependable	fickle	steadfast
3	**plausible**	correct	probable	unconvincing
4	**perish**	live	decay	freeze
5	**vanish**	materialise	polish	blemish
6	**juvenile**	childlike	youthful	mature
7	**ragged**	torn	pristine	old-fashioned
8	**beguile**	amuse	trick	repel
9	**ample**	enough	insufficient	plenty
10	**bygone**	ancient	recent	friendly

		A	B	C
11	**dishevel**	untidy	disarray	neaten
12	**melodramatic**	aggressive	enthusiastic	subdued
13	**frail**	feeble	brawny	amiable
14	**consequential**	insignificant	resultant	momentous
15	**illustrious**	unknown	infamous	empowered
16	**courteous**	chivalrous	rude	complicated
17	**inept**	unattractive	beautiful	competent
18	**disparate**	unconnected	similar	distinct
19	**doting**	ugly	adorable	uncaring
20	**cheerful**	bored	pessimistic	neglectful

Test 5 - Antonyms: Opposite Words

5 minutes

Choose one word out of the four options that means the opposite or nearly the opposite to the word on the left.

Example				
Word	A	Ⓑ	C	D
object	item	agree	reject	artefact

	Word	A	B	C	D
1	inattentive	deceitful	dreamy	goading	observant
2	indecipherable	messy	incomplete	legible	complete
3	nuisance	hindrance	annoyance	help	nightmare
4	understate	criticise	exaggerate	retort	complicate
5	detriment	advantage	prejudice	mischief	disservice
6	awkward	difficult	comfortable	easy	uneasy
7	aid	help	succour	guide	hindrance
8	varied	assorted	different	uniform	miscellaneous
9	humility	funny	modesty	unsociable	pride
10	squalor	cleanliness	discreet	ancient	original

Test 5 - Antonyms: Opposite Words

....continued

		A	**B**	**C**	**D**
11	**grotesque**	peculiar	horrible	beautiful	homely
12	**jittery**	curious	anxious	thrilled	relaxed
13	**composed**	flustered	balanced	poised	calm
14	**wicked**	evil	virtuous	naughty	tardy
15	**chivalrous**	rude	crafty	complimentary	kind
16	**creditable**	deserving	unknown	courteous	deplorable
17	**cynical**	argumentative	optimistic	pessimistic	cowardly
18	**correct**	rectified	accurate	erroneous	positive
19	**chaotic**	orderly	excessive	expansive	enthusiastic
20	**fraudulent**	terrible	honest	fiendish	boring

Test 6 - Antonyms: Opposite Words

6 minutes

Choose one word out of the five options that means the opposite or nearly the opposite to the word on the left.

Example					
Word	**A**	**(B)**	**C**	**D**	**E**
absent	away	present	never	together	today

		A	B	C	D	E
1	**liberate**	encourage	confine	follow	permit	concern
2	**responsible**	courageous	confused	ashamed	indifferent	reckless
3	**disadvantage**	occurrence	impairment	threshold	benefit	restriction
4	**heroism**	strength	weakness	defeat	success	cowardice
5	**serious**	polite	impolite	trivial	calm	enraged
6	**heighten**	increase	optimise	enhance	enlarge	reduce
7	**elevate**	hoist	lower	enlarge	maximise	heave
8	**discouraging**	weird	interesting	inspiring	appalling	rotten
9	**support**	maintain	promotion	opposition	foundation	endorsement
10	**loath**	keen	averse	resistant	free	reluctant

		A	**B**	**C**	**D**	**E**
11	**acceptance**	popularity	rejection	tolerance	recognition	acknowledgment
12	**plain**	basic	grand	ugly	reserved	simple
13	**lure**	deter	encourage	loiter	coax	tempt
14	**principal**	minor	central	chief	prime	focal
15	**obscure**	remove	simplify	stop	muddle	block
16	**outdated**	beautiful	ancient	old	modern	unfashionable
17	**alfresco**	closed	open	indoor	outside	venue
18	**wholly**	maximum	finally	cumulative	entirely	partly
19	**peril**	threat	danger	certain	safety	frightened
20	**temporary**	insignificant	infinite	important	slight	short-term

Test 7 - Antonyms: Opposite Words

7 minutes

Choose one pair out of the four options that are opposite or nearly opposite in meaning.

Example	A	despicable	repugnant	**(B)**	loathsome	delightful
	C	detestable	abhorrent	D	odious	obnoxious

1	A	scan	study	B	examine	survey
	C	rescue	free	D	convinced	sceptical
2	A	programme	scheme	B	absent	found
	C	avert	avoid	D	spectrum	order
3	A	segment	piece	B	vendor	seller
	C	seduce	tempt	D	sense	stupidity
4	A	dramatic	shocking	B	liberate	seize
	C	decision	judgement	D	solemn	earnest
5	A	coincidence	chance	B	premature	late
	C	fateful	unlucky	D	critical	important
6	A	broken	fragmented	B	intact	operational
	C	thriving	prosperous	D	development	decay
7	A	suspect	trustworthy	B	questionable	doubtful
	C	practical	logical	D	illiterate	ignorant
8	A	aptitude	inability	B	view	perception
	C	cognition	reasoning	D	intuition	awareness
9	A	ponder	wonder	B	wander	meander
	C	fitness	weakness	D	strength	vigour
10	A	belief	conviction	B	misgivings	trust
	C	sordid	despicable	D	rundown	squalid

Test 7 - Antonyms: Opposite Words

....continued

11	A	fixed	arranged	B	bravado	confidence
	C	goad	provoke	D	terrify	reassure

12	A	thrill	excite	B	maltreat	hurt
	C	scorn	admire	D	belittle	ridicule

13	A	preen	groom	B	tidy	unkempt
	C	shabby	ragged	D	dishevelled	aged

14	A	inform	update	B	betray	report
	C	advise	help	D	confiscate	relinquish

15	A	greed	envy	B	fury	placidity
	C	still	sedate	D	covet	crave

16	A	prevail	fail	B	overcome	conquer
	C	defeated	misplaced	D	evaded	escaped

17	A	appoint	hire	B	retain	preserve
	C	save	hoard	D	forgive	condemn

18	A	success	sensation	B	realise	comprehend
	C	collect	scatter	D	fulfil	achieve

19	A	groan	moan	B	snigger	grin
	C	smug	humble	D	frown	scowl

20	A	spectacular	inspiring	B	classy	quick
	C	function	operate	D	fussy	understated

BLANK PAGE

FIRST PAST THE POST®

Word Definitions

Marking Grid: Test 8															
Question	1	2	3	4	5	6	7	8	9	10	11	12	13	14	15
✓ ✗															
Question	16	17	18	19	20	21	22	23	24	25	26	27	28	29	30	Total
✓ ✗																/30

Choose the best option that offers the best definition of the word on the left.

Example	A	B	C	D
arrogant	a sense of superiority	a feeling of fear	a humble person	an unkind person

		A	B	C	D
1	morose	a large increase	a group of foolish people	a small piece	glum or moody
2	precocious	developed beyond one's years	attention seeking	detailed and elegant	to be insensitive
3	vacant	impressive and outstanding	replaced by something inferior	unoccupied	to leave
4	unrequited	not returned	to refrain from leaving	never stopping	unequalled
5	tributary	showing respect	a small stream flowing into a larger one	a Roman representative	a contender or champion
6	notorious	an excellent reputation	to tell or inform	a new commodity	infamous
7	negligible	possessing the quality of an ambassador	the outcome of a bargain	to ignore	of little or no importance
8	inadvertent	unintentional	the period preceding Christmas	mistaken or incorrect	to not provide enough
9	bequeath	located under another object	an aristocratic position	to formally endow	temporary loan
10	awe	expressing pity	exaggerated wonder	an ache	offensive or cruel

		A	**B**	**C**	**D**
11	ominous	a politician	an expression of happiness	feeling of gloom	member of a group
12	translucent	clearly aligned	hard to understand	dirty or cloudy	allowing light to pass through
13	abbreviate	making a special effort	to scold someone	extended vocabulary	to shorten a word
14	contempt	a show of gratitude	a show of affection	a blockage	displaying a dislike of someone
15	predicament	a forecast of the future	an unfortunate situation	a currency	the expected outcome
16	empathise	to draw attention to	to give priority to	an informal greeting	to identify with a something or someone
17	stimulus	giving momentum to	to express concisely	an exciting event	a poison
18	retaliate	the selling of goods	to keep possession of	responding in an aggressive manner	slow in development
19	overwrought	elaborately detailed	anxious and unsettled	constructed from iron	to amend or improve
20	naive	mentally undeveloped	lacking in worldly sophistication	relating to the nervous system	a medieval courtier

		A	B	C	D
21	tolerate	to endure	to praise	to become angry	to refuse
22	bereavement	unhappiness	a type of councillor	a period of time	experiencing loss
23	wane	to shrink	a pitiful amount	to complain	a crescent shape
24	adulation	being fond of	prolonged applause	admiration or praise	to forewarn
25	debauchery	of questionable certainty	indulging in excess	being frugal	rich and famous
26	affinity	being excessively likeable	to feign surprise	a sacred icon	experiencing harmony
27	decorum	civilised behaviour	having been decorated	elaborate and precious	to agree
28	monotonous	of one colour	tedious	inventive or new	focusing one a single idea
29	mercantile	displaying the qualities of mercury	unnecessarily cruel	relating to trade	fickle
30	enmity	a group of strangers	a state of hatred or mistrust	aggressiveness	to belong

FIRST PAST THE POST®

Category Fit

Marking Grid: Test 8															
Question	1	2	3	4	5	6	7	8	9	10	11	12	13	14	15
✓ ✗															
Question	16	17	18	19	20	21	22	23	24	25	26	27	28	29	30	Total
✓ ✗																/30

Test 9 - Category Fit

Select the group that the given word belongs to.

Example	A	(B)	C	D
diamond	clothing	stone	food	drink

		A	B	C	D
1	jacuzzi	bath	swimming pool	food	clothing
2	bazaar	transport	country	reaction	marketplace
3	monarchy	currency	government	building	instrument
4	spectacles	doctor	eyes	eyeware	work
5	asteroid	rock	science	medication	alien
6	democracy	business	product	service	government
7	gazebo	reptile	name	structure	fuel
8	trout	water	sport	animal	lake
9	pacific	healthcare	education	ocean	emotion
10	typhoon	weather	animal	earthquake	air

		A	B	C	D
11	dam	waterworks	clothing	place	fire
12	protagonist	technology	character	science	art
13	locket	lock	jewellery	metal	vegetable
14	easel	wood	nature	building	tool
15	ramekin	crockery	forest	book	country
16	sphynx	statue	animal	country	myth
17	mosaic	history	art	culture	science
18	rhapsody	material	emotion	poetry	photographs
19	the milky way	universe	chocolate	toys	holiday
20	zodiac	calendar	stars	sign	planet

		A	B	C	D
21	**chancellor**	job	currency	animal	vehicle
22	**ash**	cigarette	addiction	pipe	tree
22	**wimple**	fear	dress	clothing	country
24	**meringue**	food	song	drink	chemical
25	**detergent**	washing	job	chemical	vehicle
26	**hovel**	dwelling	room	animal	soil
27	**cavalry**	animal	war	job	food
28	**aerobics**	lycra	game	exercise	health
29	**iguana**	reptile	fruit	island	drink
30	**leprechaun**	food	myth	illness	farming

Test 10 - Mixed Test

(100 Questions)

 28 minutes

Marking Grid: Page 28-29																				
Question	1	2	3	4	5	6	7	8	9	10	1	2	3	4	5	6	7	8	9	10	Total
✓ ✗																					/20

Marking Grid: Page 30-31																				
Question	1	2	3	4	5	6	7	8	9	10	1	2	3	4	5	6	7	8	9	10	Total
✓ ✗																					/20

Marking Grid: Page 32-33																				
Question	1	2	3	4	5	6	7	8	9	10	1	2	3	4	5	6	7	8	9	10	Total
✓ ✗																					/20

Marking Grid: Page 34-35																				
Question	1	2	3	4	5	6	7	8	9	10	1	2	3	4	5	6	7	8	9	10	Total
✓ ✗																					/20

Marking Grid: Page 36-37																				
Question	1	2	3	4	5	6	7	8	9	10	1	2	3	4	5	6	7	8	9	10	Total
✓ ✗																					/20

	Overall /100

Synonyms: Similar Words - Choose one word out of the three options that means the same or nearly the same as the word on the left.

Example Word	A	B	C
exasperate	infuriate	express	choke

	Word	A	B	C
1	apprehension	desire	comprehension	fear
2	celestial	deformed	heavenly	hellish
3	anecdote	story	travel	holiday
4	gradient	slope	flat	perpendicular
5	anticipate	worry	fear	expect
6	horde	crowd	individual	accumulate
7	gaunt	ugly	thin	fat
8	demeanour	interest	speech	behaviour
9	shabby	beautiful	pristine	scruffy
10	hoax	truth	trick	treat

Synonyms: Similar Words - Choose one word out of the four options that means the same or nearly the same as the word on the left.

Example				
Word	A	B	C	D
endure	detain	enlighten	perturbed	undergo

	Word	A	B	C	D
1	saturate	starve	frequent	soak	dry
2	distorted	contorted	deported	exported	lucid
3	insufficient	excessive	scanty	profuse	refuge
4	commotion	consolation	composure	uproar	pacific
5	summit	minimum	level	trough	peak
6	meagre	sparse	liberal	inexhaustible	prolific
7	regal	normal	majestic	downtrodden	subdued
8	happiness	despondency	gloom	contentment	malaise
9	sensible	impractical	foolish	unaware	level-headed
10	decipher	encrypt	interpret	conceal	decode

Synonyms: Similar Words - Choose one word out of the five options that means the same or nearly the same as the word on the left.

Example	Word	A	Ⓑ	C	D	E
	wither	flourish	wilt	brandish	capture	create

		A	B	C	D	E
1	giddy	steady	sensible	ridiculed	dizzy	glad
2	harmony	dissonance	fluctuate	disagreement	conflict	peace
3	criticise	condemn	approve	praise	announce	delude
4	intuition	learning	hunch	scholar	intellect	curiosity
5	jostle	push	complain	concur	assent	joke
6	tousled	attractive	glamorous	shiny	knotted	lengthy
7	literary	visual	scholarly	popular	informal	meaningless
8	livid	lucid	plain	lively	sporadic	enraged
9	malicious	sumptuous	benevolent	vengeful	obliging	gracious
10	vacant	empty	freedom	sly	snide	active

Synonyms: Similar Words - Choose one word from each set that are most similar in meaning.

Example					
	Set 1			Set 2	
A	B	C	D	E	F
assess	phrase	symbol	voice	emblem	polarise

Set 1   **Set 2**

	A	B	C	D	E	F
1	leaf	camaraderie	steam	friendship	affirm	confirm
2	impartial	ale	unfair	female	child	neutral
3	reek	garlic	clothes	juniper	stench	floral
4	lavender	blustery	drink	rainbow	peanut	beverage
5	relations	door	handle	office	job	family
6	colossal	shrew	tornado	cyclone	composure	downfall
7	grin	joy	mood	ambience	narrowed	eyebrow
8	flabbergast	grimace	confused	giggle	beam	sneer
9	scowl	wince	remove	attach	build	detach
10	hoard	ecstasy	keep	elation	smart	dispel

Antonyms: Opposite Words - Choose one word out of the three options that means the opposite or nearly the opposite to the word on the left.

Example Word	A	Ⓑ	C
curtail	reduce	permit	deprive

	Word	A	B	C
1	**momentary**	short	fleeting	constant
2	**infinite**	limited	spacious	broad
3	**impulsive**	cautious	occasional	always
4	**incense**	placate	exasperate	amuse
5	**ambiguous**	vague	clear	radical
6	**aristocratic**	superior	negligent	lowly
7	**downcast**	senile	noble	elated
8	**lax**	strict	careless	jovial
9	**solemn**	stern	cheerful	concerned
10	**acknowledge**	ignore	admit	consider

Antonyms: Opposite Words - Choose one word out of the four options that means the opposite or nearly the opposite to the word on the left.

Example				
Word	A	B	Ⓒ	D
charming	attractive	charismatic	repulsive	notable

	Word	A	B	C	D
1	unfortunate	marvellous	grievous	hasty	lucky
2	malicious	benevolent	bitter	mean	muddled
3	odious	gruesome	repulsive	lengthy	delightful
4	quarrelsome	tragic	rebellious	peaceable	worried
5	ruinous	miserable	advantageous	luxurious	destructive
6	tedious	compelling	dull	banal	flat
7	wrathful	jealous	calm	vexed	saddened
8	lenient	harsh	suspicious	forlorn	argumentative
9	bruised	uncomfortable	offended	unscathed	indignant
10	riled	appeased	angry	quizzical	protesting

Test 10 - Mixed Test

....continued

Antonyms: Opposite Words - Choose one word out of the five options that means the opposite or nearly the opposite to the word on the left.

Example Word	A	B	C	D	E
lackadaisical	careful	bored	interested	active	careless

	Word	A	B	C	D	E
1	vain	modest	irritating	conceited	dramatic	honest
2	potent	disgusting	smelly	strong	weak	delicious
3	protest	rally	support	argue	challenge	profess
4	drowsy	tired	silent	alert	solemn	fragile
5	spontaneous	instantaneous	quickly	impulsive	focused	planned
6	deterrent	incentive	check	restraint	curb	abhor
7	elastic	stretchy	rigid	morose	flexible	supple
8	eloquent	friendly	fluent	expressive	inarticulate	persuasive
9	thaw	relax	friendly	freeze	melt	soften
10	masked	unclear	concealed	manic	fraudulent	exposed

Test 10 - Mixed Test

....continued

Antonyms: Opposite Words - Choose one pair out of the four options that are opposite in meaning.

Example

	A	nourishing	beneficial	B	inconvenience	burden
	C	stupefied	dazed	(D)	renowned	unknown

1	A	dimension	size	B	precision	clumsy
	C	tourist	attraction	D	adjust	modify
2	A	signature	initial	B	forge	create
	C	valuable	pointless	D	challenge	battle
3	A	attempt	try	B	variety	sorted
	C	engulfed	frozen	D	scorching	arctic
4	A	extraordinary	mundane	B	immerse	swamp
	C	destroy	unsettled	D	distinctive	interesting
5	A	descent	incline	B	supreme	angelic
	C	extinct	non-existent	D	memorise	forget
6	A	approach	retreat	B	permission	admission
	C	ravenous	discomfort	D	straightened	proud
7	A	fascinate	scintillate	B	digress	interest
	C	deliberate	unintentional	D	exclude	reform
8	A	discourage	motivate	B	transform	modify
	C	approximate	dubious	D	judge	contact
9	A	original	pioneer	B	infamous	criminal
	C	highly	prestigious	D	reality	fantasy
10	A	qualified	educated	B	participate	involve
	C	disguise	secrecy	D	planned	spontaneous

Word Definitions - Choose the option that offers the best definition of the word on the left.

Example Word	A	B	C	D
arrogant	(A) a sense of superiority	a feeling of fear	a humble person	an unkind person

		A	B	C	D
1	camaraderie	pertaining to cameras	friendship	a favourable occurrence	an authority in a specific field
2	censure	a report	to remove explicit content	a religious ritual	to criticise severely
3	flourish	to prosper	excessive confidence	relating to flowers	a group of birds
4	garbled	to speak quickly	confused	to make a bet	to collect together
5	vanquish	to disappear	to fail or lose	to totally defeat	an assortment
6	abstain	to disappear	to opt-out	to totally defeat	an assortment
7	deficient	relating to finance	without doubt	less than one	lacking in something
8	whim	a wager	a bone in the upper arm	a sudden fancy	a catastrophe
9	deliberate	to consider thoroughly	a personal message	being unclear	to wait
10	capricious	a cheerful disposition	inconsistency	lacking respect	cruel or unkind

Category Fit - Select the group that the given word belongs to.

Example				
Word	A	Ⓑ	C	D
diamond	clothing	stone	food	drink

		A	B	C	D
1	**sonnet**	vehicle	poetry	clothes	holiday
2	**jargon**	transport	language	kitchen	nature
3	**canary**	food	stationary	animal	country
4	**novella**	reference	fiction	library	magazine
5	**colosseum**	theme park	settlement	instrument	architecture
6	**tandem**	instrument	vehicle	fruit	literature
7	**artichoke**	food	sport	organ	drink
8	**catamaran**	boat	clothing	weather	food
9	**mannequin**	drink	fashion	human	festival
10	**massage**	letter	leisure	muscle	event

BLANK PAGE

Test 11 - Mixed Test

(90 Questions)

 26 minutes

Marking Grid: Page 40-41																				
Question	1	2	3	4	5	6	7	8	9	10	1	2	3	4	5	6	7	8	9	10	Total
✓ ✗																					/20

Marking Grid: Page 42-43																				
Question	1	2	3	4	5	6	7	8	9	10	1	2	3	4	5	6	7	8	9	10	Total
✓ ✗																					/20

Marking Grid: Page 44-45																				
Question	1	2	3	4	5	6	7	8	9	10	1	2	3	4	5	6	7	8	9	10	Total
																					/20

Marking Grid: Page 46-47																				
Question	1	2	3	4	5	6	7	8	9	10	1	2	3	4	5	6	7	8	9	10	Total
✓ ✗																					/20

Marking Grid: Page 48												
Question	1	2	3	4	5	6	7	8	9	10	Total		Overall
✓ ✗											/10		/90

Test 11 Mixed Test

26 minutes

Synonyms: Similar Words - Choose one word out of the three options that means the same or nearly the same as the word on the left.

Example	Word	(A)	B	C
	admit	confess	pursue	retract

		A	B	C
1	hoarse	husky	pronounced	enunciated
2	immaculate	dusty	worn	pristine
3	pardon	sanction	blame	exonerate
4	brittle	large	frail	sturdy
5	question	interrogate	relax	accept
6	jeopardy	question	danger	safety
7	rancid	rotten	potent	flavourful
8	intrepid	fearless	fearful	steady
9	melodious	sad	mute	tuneful
10	resemblance	likeness	unique	strange

Test 11 - Mixed Test

....continued

Synonyms: Similar Words - Choose one word out of the four options that means the same or nearly the same as the word on the left.

Example Word	A	B	C	D
expressionless	**(A)** impassive	B repulsed	C mute	D gaunt

#	Word	A	B	C	D
1	sever	clarify	cut	repair	maintain
2	bestow	grant	receive	enjoy	inherit
3	kindle	entice	exhaust	extinguish	ignite
4	foreshadow	predict	hide	deceive	evaluate
5	disturb	intensify	inform	interrupt	accept
6	rigid	soft	stiff	flexible	relaxed
7	serpentine	mammal	windy	straight	amphibian
8	mob	crowd	separate	solitary	individual
9	lessen	aggravate	worsen	quicken	alleviate
10	devastate	rescue	ruin	supreme	salvation

Synonyms: Similar Words - Choose one word out of the five options that means the same or nearly the same as the word on the left.

Example						
	Word	A	B	C	Ⓓ	E
	ambition	uncertain	insincere	incompetent	aspiration	nightmare

		A	B	C	D	E
1	manoeuvre	stalemate	inactive	debate	despair	guide
2	canny	devious	shrewd	balanced	ridiculous	glorious
3	avert	supplement	hostile	avoid	secret	hidden
4	alter	sustain	support	preserve	adjust	conserve
5	enigmatic	awesome	amazing	confusing	mysterious	careful
6	ambitious	failure	easy	nonchalant	reluctant	determined
7	bluff	coax	ruse	blemish	frenzy	mystery
8	fit	termination	compacted	athletic	opposition	incapable
9	lapse	gap	success	race	rise	congregation
10	considerate	thorough	discourteous	peculiar	thoughtless	sympathetic

Test 11 - Mixed Test

....continued

Antonyms: Opposite Words - Choose one word out of the three options that means the opposite or nearly the opposite to the word on the left.

Example		A	B	C
	attentive	vigilant	alert	**(C)** thoughtless

		A	B	C
1	**viable**	potential	obstacle	impractical
2	**taxing**	effortless	controversial	practical
3	**intolerant**	yearning	patient	distant
4	**conventional**	ideal	representative	unusual
5	**irrevocable**	hopeless	reversible	superlative
6	**cohesion**	union	disagreement	unanimity
7	**mirth**	hearth	glee	sorrow
8	**miserable**	benevolent	buoyant	confused
9	**shy**	diffident	confident	nervous
10	**grand**	notable	begrudging	uninspiring

Test 11 - Mixed Test

....continued

Antonyms: Opposite Words - Choose one word out of the four options that means the opposite or nearly the opposite to the word on the left.

Example	Word	(A)	B	C	D
	tangible	abstract	tactile	palpable	perceptible

		A	B	C	D
1	**courtesy**	respectability	rudeness	knowledge	splendour
2	**unanimous**	divided	unison	social	private
3	**burdensome**	substantial	opaque	light	heavy
4	**monotonous**	toneless	soporific	varied	tiring
5	**broad**	large	tall	narrow	small
6	**cheap**	inexpensive	ugly	unnecessary	dear
7	**frugal**	thrifty	scarce	extravagant	minimal
8	**daunting**	comfortable	discouraging	underwhelming	eerie
9	**stagnant**	paused	sluggish	stilting	active
10	**folly**	foolishness	wisdom	uncertainty	confidence

Test 11 - Mixed Test

....continued

Antonyms: Opposite Words - Choose one word out of the five options that means the opposite or nearly the opposite to the word on the left.

Example Word	A	B	C	D	E
unambiguous	(A) vague	ambidextrous	confusing	precise	deliberate

	Word	A	B	C	D	E
1	generosity	avarice	kindness	charitable	abundance	interest
2	woe	misery	joy	confusion	anguish	anger
3	wicked	grim	strenuous	terrifying	secured	kind
4	lawful	legal	valid	illegal	permissible	legitimate
5	confused	irrational	insane	muddled	lucid	addled
6	lull	agitate	quieten	soothe	hush	calm
7	synthetic	fake	natural	manufactured	artificial	expensive
8	ornate	showy	fancy	plain	embellished	delicate
9	ridicule	compliment	criticise	satire	mock	scorn
10	rife	universal	rare	dangerous	unknown	widespread

Antonyms: Opposite Words - Choose one pair out of the four options that are opposite in meaning.

Example					
A	categorise	sort	(B)	hero	outlaw
C	trinket	ornament	D	alternative	other

1	A	advertise	market	B	foundation	structure
	C	weight	heavy	D	pollute	clean
2	A	reassured	concerned	B	gleam	sparkle
	C	pierce	cut	D	necessary	obligation
3	A	vanish	identify	B	cast	preserve
	C	strength	limitations	D	destination	goal
4	A	involve	decline	B	serious	farce
	C	thorough	vigorous	D	insure	pronounce
5	A	purchase	exchange	B	translate	property
	C	wash	cleanliness	D	effective	faulty
6	A	attention	focus	B	comfort	console
	C	friend	companion	D	concur	resist
7	A	synchronise	coordinate	B	harmonise	conflict
	C	reasonable	logical	D	correspond	coincide
8	A	educate	teach	B	scold	praise
	C	annoy	irritate	D	caution	discipline
9	A	rigorous	lax	B	rough	coarse
	C	smooth	even	D	ill	poorly
10	A	gracious	polite	B	reserved	detached
	C	free	restricted	D	conventional	ordinary

Word Definitions - Choose the option that offers the best definition of the word on the left.

Example				
	Ⓐ	B	C	D
arrogant	a sense of superiority	a feeling of fear	a humble person	an unkind person

		A	B	C	D
1	nonchalant	careless	aggressive	friendly	insolent
2	colloquial	from a colony	casual and conversational	an assortment of objects	being irresponsible
3	pretentious	stylish and elegant	involved in theatre	shyness	affected
4	prejudice	foreboding	deep in thought	an unfair judgement	an insult
5	zenith	a public leader	an obstacle	requiring more	the highest point
6	proficient	able to do well	a career	to calibrate	a well educated person
7	wither	a question word	to fade and die	without a clear plan	uncertain
8	rowdy	imitating a crowd	arranged in a straight line	loud and unruly	disagreeing
9	scarce	an insufficient amount	the state of terror	a great distance away	to frighten someone
10	precaution	to give a warning	acting uncertainly	of great value	intended to prevent an event

Test 11 - Mixed Test

....continued

Category Fit - Select the group that the given word belongs to.

Example Word	A	B	C	D
diamond	clothing	(stone)	food	drink

		A	B	C	D
1	**coach**	tool	city	building	job
2	**dime**	place	grain	city	currency
3	**rickshaw**	fuel	vehicle	knife	liquid
4	**carousel**	food	building	transport	ride
5	**mouse**	tool	food	animal	forest
6	**magnesium**	vitamin	magnet	metal	food
7	**brochure**	clothing	document	holiday	jewellery
8	**eucalyptus**	tree	planet	chemical	sign
9	**quinoa**	tribe	grain	country	tree
10	**caravan**	building	machine	transport	food

Test 12 - Mixed Test

(100 Questions)

28 minutes

Marking Grid: Page 50-51																				
Question	1	2	3	4	5	6	7	8	9	10	1	2	3	4	5	6	7	8	9	10	Total
✓ ✗																					/20

Marking Grid: Page 51-53																				
Question	1	2	3	4	5	6	7	8	9	10	1	2	3	4	5	6	7	8	9	10	Total
✓ ✗																					/20

Marking Grid: Page 54-55																				
Question	1	2	3	4	5	6	7	8	9	10	1	2	3	4	5	6	7	8	9	10	Total
																					/20

Marking Grid: Page 56-57																				
Question	1	2	3	4	5	6	7	8	9	10	1	2	3	4	5	6	7	8	9	10	Total
✓ ✗																					/20

Marking Grid: Page 58-59																				
Question	1	2	3	4	5	6	7	8	9	10	1	2	3	4	5	6	7	8	9	10	Total
✓ ✗																					/20

	Overall
	/100

Synonyms: Similar Words - Choose one word out of the three options that means the same or nearly the same as the word on the left.

Example	Word	A	B	C
	healthy	lethargic	tasty	nutritious

	Word	A	B	C
1	poisonous	rare	curable	venomous
2	stormy	tempestuous	rocky	steady
3	retaliate	suppress	forgive	react
4	gruesome	grisly	grizzly	ghostly
5	disorder	argument	order	chaos
6	deride	hide	show	mock
7	impair	repair	damage	faulty
8	aghast	ghostly	stunned	guiltless
9	canter	pause	run	meander
10	foul	impish	courteous	repulsive

Synonyms: Similar Words - **Choose one word out of the four options that means the same or nearly the same as the word on the left.**

Example				
Word	A	B	C	D
blue	joyful	sad	colour	purple

		A	B	C	D
1	emigration	arrival	relocation	transient	permanent
2	eminent	illustrious	imminent	pervading	unknown
3	loath	fearful	reluctant	vile	positive
4	steep	steady	flood	marinate	quicken
5	diminutive	petite	grand	colossal	vast
6	fiasco	celebration	party	debacle	tango
7	quiet	piercing	loud	reticent	rotated
8	articulate	clumsy	embellished	inaudible	coherent
9	gossip	insult	chatter	silence	compliment
10	brief	persuasive	boring	succinct	lengthy

Test 12 - Mixed Test

....continued

Synonyms: Similar Words - Choose one word out of the five options that means the same or nearly the same as the word on the left.

Example						
	Word	A	B	C	Ⓓ	E
	tight	skinny	loose	small	fitted	baggy

	Word	A	B	C	D	E
1	hue	sunrise	cave	shade	blackened	forest
2	litter	plastic	supplement	appetiser	refuse	bonus
3	numb	furious	unfeeling	jovial	gaunt	plump
4	craggy	barren	hidden	smooth	wilderness	rocky
5	restless	formal	placid	agitated	confused	casual
6	chasm	canyon	puddle	forbidden	engagement	security
7	prone	terrifying	witch	guarded	motionless	exploration
8	pompous	haughty	modest	enormous	meek	scrawny
9	unified	underwhelmed	exaggerated	divided	surplus	joined
10	veer	stationary	swerve	cycle	voyage	ignore

Synonyms: Similar Words - Choose one word from each set that are most similar in meaning.

Example						
	Set 1				**Set 2**	
	A	B	C	D	E	F
	peaceful	calm	anxious	angry	worried	angle

	Set 1			**Set 2**		
	A	B	C	D	E	F
1	mayday	manic	morose	payday	greed	melancholy
	A	B	C	D	E	F
2	exile	patriot	audience	banish	welcome	ignore
	A	B	C	D	E	F
3	dusk	sunrise	moonshine	cloudy	birds	dawn
	A	B	C	D	E	F
4	meat	gossip	hunger	hollered	thirst	rumour
	A	B	C	D	E	F
5	sip	tepid	slurp	lemonade	lukewarm	icy
	A	B	C	D	E	F
6	cackle	glum	stationary	gum	chuckle	fluctuate
	A	B	C	D	E	F
7	bulging	furnace	vehicle	protruding	dome	pedestrian
	A	B	C	D	E	F
8	succulent	education	necklace	essay	treasure	juicy
	A	B	C	D	E	F
9	fly	drop	soar	style	fashion	release
	A	B	C	D	E	F
10	ruler	pliable	metallic	scissors	flexible	lengthy

Test 12 - Mixed Test

....continued

Antonyms: Opposite Words - Choose one word out of the three options that means the opposite or nearly the opposite to the word on the left.

Example			
Word	(A)	B	C
continuous	intermittent	continual	contained

	Word	A	B	C
1	doubt	sceptic	mistrust	certainty
2	audacious	concerned	courageous	timid
3	disingenuous	punctual	honest	devious
4	exorbitant	cheap	costly	reasonable
5	progress	continuation	introduce	regress
6	conceal	screen	divulge	camouflage
7	putrid	fresh	rotten	matured
8	scarce	unusual	abundant	meagre
9	permanent	eternal	enduring	temporary
10	boost	discourage	motivate	lift

Antonyms: Opposite Words - Choose one word out of the four options that means the opposite or nearly the opposite to the word on the left.

Example				
Word	A	B	C	D
predictable	confusing	unexpected	unsurprising	expected

	Word	A	B	C	D
1	**greed**	jealousy	envy	moderation	gluttony
2	**barren**	sterile	desolate	waste	fertile
3	**compulsory**	negative	voluntary	positive	required
4	**faulty**	eventual	consistent	flawless	defective
5	**wax**	wane	shiny	pale	comfortable
6	**exposed**	bare	sheltered	public	vulnerable
7	**economical**	judging	conclusive	rich	wasteful
8	**slack**	relaxed	slovenly	dull	taut
9	**improved**	declined	recuperated	corrected	amended
10	**deteriorate**	waste	fade	depreciate	recover

Test 12 - Mixed Test
....continued

Antonyms: Opposite Words - Choose one word out of the five options that means the opposite or nearly the opposite to the word on the left.

Example Word	A	B	C	D	(E)
improbable	clueless	surprising	possible	impossible	likely

	Word	A	B	C	D	E
1	bleak	inhospitable	deserted	harsh	barren	hopeful
2	feasible	dreary	impossible	passionate	fanciful	impractical
3	shameful	honourable	spoilt	hopeless	poor	standard
4	integrate	involve	communicate	separate	merge	join
5	rustic	homely	rough	pastoral	sophisticated	urban
6	drastic	serious	extreme	radical	dire	mild
7	streamlined	efficient	slick	cumbersome	natural	smooth
8	endorse	disapprove	agree	assist	promote	support
9	rational	overwhelming	realistic	sane	illogical	wise
10	eclectic	unhappy	regulated	varied	diverse	restricted

Antonyms: Opposite Words - Choose one pair out of the four options that are opposite in meaning.

Example						
	A	loud	noisy	B	cautious	wary
	(C)	voluntary	obligatory	D	peace	tranquillity

1	A	secluded	confined	B	protected	sheltered
	C	individual	collective	D	cooperative	helpful

2	A	wild	tame	B	continued	progressed
	C	resolved	settled	D	organised	ordered

3	A	troubled	worried	B	agitated	upset
	C	carefree	cheery	D	nonchalant	fretful

4	A	incredible	outrageous	B	polite	weird
	C	suspect	trustworthy	D	ferocious	vicious

5	A	truancy	attendance	B	isolation	segregation
	C	monitored	supervised	D	accomplice	assistant

6	A	havoc	mayhem	B	disenchant	inspire
	C	reel	lurch	D	luxury	delight

7	A	primp	preen	B	peruse	examine
	C	fringe	edge	D	eccentric	ordinary

8	A	spontaneous	free	B	volatile	stable
	C	released	liberated	D	restricted	constrained

9	A	hefty	bulky	B	slight	brawny
	C	awkward	clumsy	D	wide	broad

10	A	justified	unfair	B	ridiculous	silly
	C	oblivious	unaware	D	practical	sensible

Test 12 - Mixed Test

....continued

Word Definitions - Choose the option that offers the best definition of the word on the left.

Example Word	A	B	C	D
arrogant	(A) a sense of superiority	a feeling of fear	a humble person	an unkind person

		A	B	C	D
1	**ostracise**	originating in	to exclude	to oppress a minority	occurring rarely
2	**palpable**	able to be felt	crushed into dust	dishonest behaviour	recklessness
3	**obstinate**	to block the progress of	being impertinent	unwilling to change	partaking in a deception
4	**travesty**	a genre of play	a great shame	a long journey	to undermine
5	**omit**	a sign of what will happen	to include	to share	to exclude
6	**beneficial**	being advantageous	kind and helpful	claiming maintenance	possessing the qualities of a friend
7	**preclude**	to summarise a body of text	beginning an activity	prevent from occurring	a small speech
8	**obsolete**	to forget	ruined	stubborn	outdated
9	**abate**	to encourage dissent	to become less	to be capable of doing	to leave behind
10	**lament**	to be physically incapable	to express sorrow	in great pain	wayward

Category Fit - Select the group that the given word belongs to.

Example				
Word	A	(B)	C	D
diamond	clothing	stone	food	drink

		A	B	C	D
1	**manuscript**	photograph	writer	text	film
2	**futon**	bedding	architecture	fuel	island
3	**satchel**	fashion	work	bag	jewellery
4	**orthodontist**	profession	medicine	religion	writer
5	**dodo**	instrument	game	animal	toys
6	**billiards**	tool	game	job	ball
7	**thyme**	river	herb	plant	vegetable
8	**ode**	country	language	poetry	vehicle
9	**tenor**	sounds	metal	plants	voice
10	**decibel**	city	music	sound	power

BLANK PAGE

FIRST PAST THE POST®

Answers

BLANK PAGE

ANSWERS

TEST 1 - Synonyms: Similar Words

Page 2	Answer	The words most similar in meaning are...
Example	C	**BREACH and CONTRAVENE**
1	B	EQUIVALENT and COUNTERPART
2	A	DESPERATE and CRAVING
3	B	ABSCOND and ESCAPE
4	C	SMOULDER and BURN
5	A	FORCIBLE and VIOLENT
6	B	PREFERENCE and FAVOURITE
7	C	TRANSFER and SHIFT
8	B	AMATEUR and NON-PROFESSIONAL
9	A	CONSCIENCE and PRINCIPLES
10	B	DISASTROUS and CATACLYSMIC
Page 3		
11	C	PREJUDICE and BIAS
12	A	EROSION and DESTRUCTION
13	C	BEMUSED and PUZZLED
14	C	BURDEN and CARGO
15	A	CLAMOROUS and LOUD
16	B	HASSLE and ANNOYANCE
17	A	CRITICISM and CONDEMNATION
18	B	PRECIPITOUS and STEEP
19	B	ABDUCT and SEIZE
20	C	BLISS and HAPPINESS

TEST 2 - Synonyms: Similar Words

Page 4	Answer	The words most similar in meaning are...
Example	B	**ANTIPATHETIC and HOSTILE**
1	C	NUTRITIOUS and HEALTHY
2	D	ORIENTATE and ALIGN
3	A	SPECTACLE and DISPLAY
4	B	UNITE and AMALGAMATE
5	D	SODDEN and SOAKED
6	A	PREPARED and ASSEMBLED
7	D	PURE and UNBLENDED
8	B	RETENTIVE and ABSORBANT
9	C	SECURE and FASTENED
10	D	OPPORTUNE and FAVOURABLE

11	C	TACTFUL and DISCREET
12	D	UPSTANDING and RESPECTABLE
13	D	TERMINATE and CEASE
14	C	ACQUAINT and FAMILIARISE
15	B	CONSOLE and COMFORT
16	A	CONTEST and DISPUTE
17	A	WORTHY and VIRTUOUS
18	B	RECKLESS and RASH
19	D	HOSPITABLE and GRACIOUS
20	C	REMOTE and DISTANT

TEST 3 - Synonyms: Similar Words

Page 6	Answer	The words most similar in meaning are...
Example	C	**DANGLE and SUSPEND**
1	E	SUPPLE and FLEXIBLE
2	B	EXCLUSIVE and SPECIAL
3	C	MEDIOCRE and AVERAGE
4	B	CORRUPT and IMMORAL
5	C	WHIM and IMPULSE
6	A	WRETCHED and UNHAPPY
7	E	FORECAST and PREDICT
8	A	FOSTER and NURTURE
9	B	CONTAMINATE and POLLUTE
10	C	BENEFICIARY and HEIR
Page 7		
11	A	BETRAYAL and TREACHERY
12	D	MYSTIFY and BEWILDER
13	A	PUNGENT and BITTER
14	B	PRETENCE and DISGUISE
15	A	COLLIDE and CRASH
16	C	CUNNING and WILY
17	C	ORDERLY and SMART
18	E	DEMURE and RESERVED
19	B	NEEDFUL and RELIANT
20	A	ENABLE and ALLOW

Test 4 - Antonyms: Opposite Words

Page 10	Answer	The words most opposite in meaning are...
Example	C	**SOCIABLE and SHY**
1	B	ANIMOSITY and GOODWILL
2	B	FAITHFUL and FICKLE
3	C	PLAUSIBLE and UNCONVINCING
4	A	PERISH and LIVE
5	A	VANISH and MATERIALISE
6	C	JUVENILE and MATURE
7	B	RAGGED and PRISTINE
8	C	BEGUILE and REPEL
9	B	AMPLE and INSUFFICIENT
10	B	BYGONE and RECENT
Page 11		
11	C	DISHEVEL and NEATEN
12	C	MELODRAMATIC and SUBDUED
13	B	FRAIL and BRAWNY
14	A	CONSEQUENTIAL and INSIGNIFICANT
15	A	ILLUSTRIOUS and UNKNOWN
16	B	COURTEOUS and RUDE
17	C	INEPT and COMPETENT
18	B	DISPARATE and SIMILAR
19	C	DOTING and UNCARING
20	B	CHEERFUL and PESSIMISTIC

Test 5 - Antonyms: Opposite Words

Page 12	Answer	The words most opposite in meaning are...
Example	B	**OBJECT and AGREE**
1	D	INATTENTIVE and OBSERVANT
2	C	INDECIPHERABLE and LEGIBLE
3	C	NUISANCE and HELP
4	B	UNDERSTATE and EXAGGERATE
5	A	DETRIMENT and ADVANTAGE
6	B	AWKWARD and COMFORTABLE
7	D	AID and HINDRANCE
8	C	VARIED and UNIFORM
9	D	HUMILITY and PRIDE
10	A	SQUALOR and CLEANLINESS

11	C	GROTESQUE and BEAUTIFUL
12	D	JITTERY and RELAXED
13	A	COMPOSED and FLUSTERED
14	B	WICKED and VIRTUOUS
15	A	CHIVALROUS and RUDE
16	D	CREDITABLE and DEPLORABLE
17	B	CYNICAL and OPTIMISTIC
18	C	CORRECT and ERRONEOUS
19	A	CHAOTIC and ORDERLY
20	B	FRAUDULENT and HONEST

Test 6 - Antonyms: Opposite Words

Page 14	Answer	The words most opposite in meaning are...
Example	B	**ABSENT and PRESENT**
1	B	LIBERATE and CONFINE
2	E	RESPONSIBLE and RECKLESS
3	D	DISADVANTAGE and BENEFIT
4	E	HEROISM and COWARDICE
5	C	SERIOUS and TRIVIAL
6	E	HEIGHTEN and REDUCE
7	B	ELEVATE and LOWER
8	C	DISCOURAGING and INSPIRING
9	C	SUPPORT and OPPOSITION
10	A	LOATH and KEEN
Page 15		
11	B	ACCEPTANCE and REJECTION
12	B	PLAIN and GRAND
13	A	LURE and DETER
14	A	PRINCIPAL and MINOR
15	B	OBSCURE and SIMPLIFY
16	D	OUTDATED and MODERN
17	D	ALFRESCO and INDOOR
18	E	WHOLLY and PARTLY
19	D	PERIL and SAFETY
20	B	TEMPORARY and INFINITE

Test 7- Antonyms: Opposite Words

Page 16	Answer	The pair of antonyms is...
Example	B	**LOATHSOME and DELIGHTFUL**
1	D	CONVINCED and SCEPTICAL
2	B	ABSENT and FOUND
3	D	SENSE and STUPIDITY
4	B	LIBERATE and SEIZE
5	B	PREMATURE and LATE
6	D	DEVELOPMENT and DECAY
7	A	SUSPECT and TRUSTWORTHY
8	A	APTITUDE and INABILITY
9	C	FITNESS and WEAKNESS
10	B	MISGIVINGS and TRUST
Page 17		
11	D	TERRIFY and REASSURE
12	C	SCORN and ADMIRE
13	B	TIDY and UNKEMPT
14	D	CONFISCATE and RELINQUISH
15	B	FURY and PLACIDITY
16	A	PREVAIL and FAIL
17	D	FORGIVE and CONDEMN
18	C	COLLECT and SCATTER
19	C	SMUG and HUMBLE
20	D	FUSSY and UNDERSTATED

Test 8 – Word Definitions

Page 20	Answer	Choose the best option that offers the best definition of the word on the left.
Example	A	**ARROGANT: closest meaning - a sense of superiority.**
1	D	MOROSE: closest meaning - glum or moody.
2	A	PRECOCIOUS: closest meaning - developed beyond one's years.
3	C	VACANT: closest meaning - unoccupied.
4	A	UNREQUITED: closest meaning - not returned.
5	B	TRIBUTARY: closest meaning - a small stream flowing into a larger one.
6	D	NOTORIOUS: closest meaning - infamous.
7	D	NEGLIGIBLE: closest meaning - of little or no importance .
8	A	INADVERTENT: closest meaning - unintentional.
9	C	BEQUEATH: closest meaning - to formally endow.
10	B	AWE: closest meaning - exaggerated wonder.
11	C	OMINOUS closest meaning: feeling of gloom
12	D	TRANSLUCENT: closest meaning - allowing light to pass through.
13	D	ABBREVIATE: closest meaning - to shorten a word.
14	D	CONTEMPT: closest meaning - displaying a dislike of someone.
15	B	PREDICAMENT: closest meaning - an unfortunate situation.
16	D	EMPATHISE: closest meaning - to identify with a something or someone.
17	A	STIMULUS: closest meaning - giving momentum to.
18	C	RETALIATE: closest meaning - responding in an agressive manner.
19	B	OVERWROUGHT: closest meaning - anxious and unsettled.
20	B	NAIVE: closest meaning - lacking in worldly sophistication.

Page 22

21	A	TOLERATE: closest meaning - to endure
22	D	BEREAVEMENT: closest meaning - experiencing loss
23	A	WANE: closest meaning - to shrink
24	C	ADULATION: closest meaning - admiration or praise
25	B	DEBAUCHERY: closest meaning - indulging in excess
26	D	AFFINITY: closest meaning - experiencing harmony
27	A	DECORUM: closest meaning - civilised behaviour
28	B	MONOTONOUS: closest meaning - tedious
29	C	MERCANTILE: closest meaning - relating to trade
30	B	ENMITY: closest meaning - a state of hatred or mistrust

Test 9 - Category Fit

Page 24		Select the group that the given word belongs to
Example	B	EMERALD belongs to the group: stone.
1	A	JACUZZI belongs to the group: bath
2	D	BAZAAR belongs to the group: marketplace
3	B	MONARCHY belongs to the group: government
4	C	SPECTACLES belongs to the group: eyewear
5	A	ASTEROID belongs to the group: rock
6	D	DEMOCRACY belongs to the group: government
7	C	GAZEBO belongs to the group: structure
8	C	TROUT belongs to the group: animal
9	C	PACIFIC belongs to the group: ocean
10	A	TYPHOON belongs to the group: weather
11	A	DAM belongs to the group: waterworks
12	B	PROTAGONIST belongs to the group: character
13	B	LOCKET belongs to the group: jewellery
14	D	EASEL belongs to the group: tool
15	A	RAMEKIN belongs to the group: crockery
16	D	SPHYNX belongs to the group: animal
17	B	MOSAIC belongs to the group: art
18	C	RHAPSODY belongs to the group: poetry
19	A	THE MILKY WAY belongs to the group: universe
20	A	ZODIAC belongs to the group: calendar
21	A	CHANCELLOR belongs to the group: job
22	D	ASH belongs to the group: tree
23	C	WIMPLE belongs to the group: clothing
24	A	MERINGUE belongs to the group: food
25	C	DETERGENT belongs to the group: chemical
26	A	HOVEL belongs to the group: dwelling
27	B	CAVALRY belongs to the group: war
28	C	AEROBICS belongs to the group: exercise
29	A	IGUANA belongs to the group: reptile
30	B	LEPRECHAUN belongs to the group: myth

Test 10 - Mixed Test

Synonyms: Similar Words
(one word out of three options)

Page 28	Answer	The words most similar in meaning are...
Example	A	**EXASPERATE and INFURIATE**
1	C	APPREHENSION and FEAR
2	B	CELESTIAL and HEAVENLY
3	A	ANECDOTE and STORY
4	A	GRADIENT and SLOPE
5	C	ANTICIPATE and EXPECT
6	A	HORDE and CROWD
7	B	GAUNT and THIN
8	C	DEMEANOUR and BEHAVIOUR
9	C	SHABBY and SCRUFFY
10	B	HOAX and TRICK

Synonyms: Similar Words
(one word out of four options)

Page 29	Answer	The words most similar in meaning are...
Example	D	**ENDURE and UNDERGO**
1	C	SATURATE and SOAK
2	A	DISTORTED and CONTORTED
3	B	INSUFFICIENT and SCANTY
4	C	COMMOTION and UPROAR
5	D	SUMMIT and PEAK
6	A	MEAGRE and SPARSE
7	B	REGAL and MAJESTIC
8	C	HAPPINESS and CONTENTMENT
9	D	SENSIBLE and LEVEL-HEADED
10	D	DECIPHER and DECODE

Synonyms: Similar Words
(one word out of five options)

Page 30	Answer	The words most similar in meaning are...
Example	B	**WITHER and WILT**
1	D	GIDDY and DIZZY
2	E	HARMONY and PEACE
3	A	CRITICISE and CONDEMN
4	B	INTUITION and HUNCH
5	A	JOSTLE and PUSH
6	D	TOUSLED and KNOTTED
7	B	LITERARY and SCHOLARLY
8	E	LIVID and ENRAGED
9	C	MALICIOUS and VENGEFUL
10	A	VACANT and EMPTY

Synonyms: Similar Words
(one word from each set)

Page 31	Answer 1	Answer 2	The words most similar in meaning are...
Example	C	E	**SYMBOL and EMBLEM**
1	B	D	CAMARADERIE and FRIENDSHIP
2	A	F	IMPARTIAL and NEUTRAL
3	A	E	REEK and STENCH
4	C	F	DRINK and BEVERAGE
5	A	F	RELATIONS and FAMILY
6	C	D	TORNADO and CLYCLONE
7	C	D	MOOD and AMBIANCE
8	B	F	GRIMACE and SNEER
9	C	F	REMOVE and DETACH
10	B	D	ECSTASY and ELATION

Antonyms: Opposite Words
(one word out of three options)

Page 32	Answer	The words most opposite in meaning are...
Example	B	**CURTAIL and PERMIT**
1	C	MOMENTARY and CONSTANT
2	A	INFINITE and LIMITED
3	A	IMPULSIVE and CAUTIOUS
4	A	INCENSE and PLACATE
5	B	AMBIGUOUS and CLEAR
6	C	ARISTOCRATIC and LOWLY
7	C	DOWNCAST and ELATED
8	A	LAX and STRICT
9	B	SOLEMN and CHEERFUL
10	A	ACKNOWLEDGE and IGNORE

Antonyms: Opposite Words
(one word out of four options)

Page 33	Answer	The words most opposite in meaning are...
Example	C	**CHARMING and REPULSIVE**
1	D	UNFORTUNATE and LUCKY
2	A	MALICIOUS and BENEVOLENT
3	D	ODIOUS and DELIGHTFUL
4	C	QUARRELSOME and PEACEABLE
5	B	RUINOUS and ADVANTAGEOUS
6	A	TEDIOUS and COMPELLING
7	B	WRATHFUL and CALM
8	A	LENIENT and HARSH
9	C	BRUISED and UNSCATHED
10	A	RILED and APPEASED

Antonyms: Opposite Words
(one word out of five options)

Page 34	Answer	The words most opposite in meaning are...
Example	A	**LACKADAISICAL and CAREFUL**
1	A	VAIN and MODEST
2	D	POTENT and WEAK
3	B	PROTEST and SUPPORT
4	C	DROWSY and ALERT
5	E	SPONTANEOUS and PLANNED
6	A	DETERRENT and INCENTIVE
7	B	ELASTIC and RIGID
8	D	ELOQUENT and INARTICULATE
9	C	THAW and FREEZE
10	E	MASKED and EXPOSED

Antonyms: Opposite Words
(one pair out of four options)

Page 35	Answer	The pair of antonyms is...
Example	D	**RENOWNED and UNKNOWN**
1	B	PRECISION and CLUMSY
2	C	VALUABLE and POINTLESS
3	D	SCORCHING and ARCTIC
4	A	EXTRAORDINARY and MUNDANE
5	D	MEMORISE and FORGET
6	A	APPROACH and RETREAT
7	C	DELIBERATE and UNINTENTIONAL
8	A	DISCOURAGE and MOTIVATE
9	D	REALITY and FANTASY
10	D	PLANNED and SPONTANEOUS

Word Definitions

Page 36	Answer	Choose the best option that offers the best definition of the word on the left.
Example	A	**ARROGANT: closest meaning - a sense of superiority.**
1	B	CAMARADERIE: closest meaning - friendship
2	D	CENSURE: closest meaning - to criticise severely
3	A	FLOURISH: closest meaning - to prosper
4	B	GARBLED: closest meaning - confused
5	C	VANQUISH: closest meaning - to totally defeat
6	B	ABSTAIN: closest meaning - to opt out
7	D	DEFICIENT: closest meaning - lacking in something
8	C	WHIM: closest meaning - a sudden fancy
9	A	DELIBERATE: closest meaning - to consider thoroughly
10	B	CAPRICIOUS: closest meaning - inconsistency

Category Fit

Page 37		Select the group that the given word belongs to.
Example	**B**	**DIAMOND belongs to the group: stone**
1	B	SONNET belongs to the group: poetry
2	B	JARGON belongs to the group: language
3	C	CANARY belongs to the group: animal
4	B	NOVELLA belongs to the group: fiction
5	D	COLOSSEUM belongs to the group: architecture
6	B	TANDEM belongs to the group: vehicle
7	A	ARTICHOKE belongs to the group: food
8	A	CATAMARAN belongs to the group: boat
9	B	MANNEQUIN belongs to the group: fashion
10	B	MASSAGE belongs to the group: leisure

Mixed Test 11

Synonyms: Similar Words
(one word out of three options)

Page 40	Answer	The words most similar in meaning are...
Example	A	**ADMIT and CONFESS**
1	A	HOARSE and HUSKY
2	C	IMMACULATE and PRISTINE
3	C	PARDON and EXONERATE
4	B	BRITTLE and FRAIL
5	A	QUESTION and INTERROGATE
6	B	JEOPARDY and DANGER
7	A	RANCID and ROTTEN
8	A	INTREPID and FEARLESS
9	C	MELODIOUS and TUNEFUL
10	A	RESEMBLANCE and LIKENESS

Synonyms: Similar Words
(one word out of four options)

Page 41	Answer	The words most similar in meaning are...
Example	A	**EXPRESSIONLESS and IMPASSIVE**
1	B	SEVER and CUT
2	A	BESTOW and GRANT
3	D	KINDLE and IGNITE
4	A	FORESHADOW and PREDICT
5	C	DISTURB and INTERRUPT
6	B	RIGID and STIFF
7	B	SERPENTINE and WINDY
8	A	MOB and CROWD
9	D	LESSEN and ALLEVIATE
10	B	DEVASTATE and RUIN

Synonyms: Similar Words
(one word out of five options)

Page 42	Answer	The words most similar in meaning are...
Example	D	**AMBITION and ASPIRATION**
1	E	MANOEUVRE and GUIDE
2	B	CANNY and SHREWD
3	C	AVERT and AVOID
4	D	ALTER and ADJUST
5	D	ENIGMATIC and MYSTERIOUS
6	E	AMBITIOUS and DETERMINED
7	B	BLUFF and RUSE
8	C	FIT and ATHLETIC
9	A	LAPSE and GAP
10	E	CONSIDERATE and SYMPATHETIC

Antonyms: Opposite Words
(one word out of three options)

Page 43	Answer	The words most opposite in meaning are...
Example	C	**ATTENTIVE and THOUGHTLESS**
1	C	VIABLE and IMPRACTICAL
2	A	TAXING and EFFORTLESS
3	B	INTOLERANT and PATIENT
4	C	CONVENTIONAL and UNUSUAL
5	B	IRREVOCABLE and REVERSIBLE
6	B	COHESION and DISAGREEMENT
7	C	MIRTH and SORROW
8	B	MISERABLE and BUOYANT
9	B	SHY and CONFIDENT
10	C	GRAND and UNINSPIRING

Antonyms: Opposite Words
(one word out of four options)

Page 44	Answer	The words most opposite in meaning are...
Example	A	**TANGIBLE and ABSTRACT**
1	B	COURTESY and RUDENESS
2	A	UNANIMOUS and DIVIDED
3	C	BURDENSOME and LIGHT
4	C	MONOTONOUS and VARIED
5	C	BROAD and NARROW
6	D	CHEAP and DEAR
7	C	FRUGAL and EXTRAVAGANT
8	A	DAUNTING and COMFORTABLE
9	D	STAGNANT and ACTIVE
10	B	FOLLY and WISDOM

Antonyms: Opposite Words
(one word out of five options)

Page 45	Answer	The words most opposite in meaning are...
Example	A	**UNAMBIGUOUS and VAGUE**
1	A	GENEROSITY and AVARICE
2	B	WOE and JOY
3	E	WICKED and KIND
4	C	LAWFUL and ILLEGAL
5	D	CONFUSED and LUCID
6	A	LULL and AGITATE
7	B	SYNTHETIC and NATURAL
8	C	ORNATE and PLAIN
9	A	RIDICULE and COMPLIMENT
10	B	RIFE and RARE

Antonyms: Opposite Words
(one pair out of four options)

Page 46	Answer	The pair of antonyms is...
Example	B	**HERO and OUTLAW**
1	D	POLLUTE and CLEAN
2	A	REASSURED and CONCERNED
3	C	STRENGTH and LIMITATIONS
4	B	SERIOUS and FARCE
5	D	EFFECTIVE and FAULTY
6	D	SURRENDER and RESIST
7	B	HARMONISE and CONFLICT
8	B	SCOLD and PRAISE
9	A	RIGOROUS and LAX
10	C	FREE and RESTRICTED

Word Definitions

Page 47	Answer	Choose the best option that offers the best definition of the word on the left
Example	A	**ARROGANT: closest meaning - a sense of superiority**
1	A	NONCHALANT: closest meaning - careless
2	B	COLLOQUIAL: closest meaning - casual and conversational
3	D	PRETENTIOUS: closest meaning - affected
4	C	PREJUDICE: closest meaning - an unfair judgement
5	D	ZENITH: closest meaning - the highest point
6	A	PROFICIENT: closest meaning - able to do well
7	B	WITHER: closest meaning - to fade and die
8	C	ROWDY: closest meaning - loud and unruly
9	A	SCARCE: closest meaning - an insufficient amount
10	D	PRECAUTION: closest meaning - intended to prevent an event

Category Fit

Page 48		Select the group that the given word belongs to
Example	**B**	**DIAMON belongs to the group: stone**
1	D	COACH belongs to the group: job
2	D	DIME belongs to the group: currency
3	B	RICKSHAW belongs to the group: vehicle
4	D	CAROUSEL belongs to the group: ride
5	C	MOUSE belongs to the group: animal
6	C	MAGNESIUM belongs to the group: metal
7	B	BROCHURE belongs to the group: document
8	A	EUCALYPTUS belongs to the group: tree
9	B	QUINOA belongs to the group: grain
10	C	CARAVAN belongs to the group: transport

Mixed Test 12

Synonyms: Similar Words
(one word out of three options)

Page 50	Answer	The words most similar in meaning are...
Example	C	**HEALTHY and NUTRITIOUS**
1	C	POISONOUS and VENOMOUS
2	A	STORMY and TEMPESTUOUS
3	C	RETALIATE and REACT
4	A	GRUESOME and GRISLY
5	C	DISORDER and CHAOS
6	C	DERIDE and MOCK
7	B	IMPAIR and DAMAGE
8	B	AGHAST and STUNNED
9	B	CANTER and RUN
10	C	FOUL and REPULSIVE

Synonyms: Similar Words
(one word out of four options)

Page 51	Answer	The words most similar in meaning are...
Example	B	**BLUE and SAD**
1	B	EMIGRATION and RELOCATION
2	A	EMINENT and ILLUSTRIOUS
3	B	LOATH and RELUCTANT
4	C	STEEP and MARINATE
5	A	DIMINUTIVE and PETITE
6	C	FIASCO and DEBACLE
7	C	QUIET and RETICENT
8	D	ARTICULATE and COHERENT
9	B	GOSSIP and CHATTER
10	C	BRIEF and SUCCINCT

Synonyms: Similar Words
(one word out of five options)

Page 52	Answer	The words most similar in meaning are...
Example	D	**TIGHT and FITTED**
1	C	HUE and SHADE
2	D	LITTER and REFUSE
3	B	NUMB and UNFEELING
4	E	CRAGGY and ROCKY
5	C	RESTLESS and AGITATED
6	A	CHASM and CANYON
7	D	PRONE and MOTIONLESS
8	A	POMPOUS and HAUGHTY
9	E	UNIFIED and JOINED
10	B	VEER and SWERVE

Synonyms: Similar Words
(one word from each set)

Page 53	Answer 1	Answer 2	The words most similar in meaning are...
Example	C	E	**ANXIOUS and WORRIED**
1	C	F	MOROSE and MELANCHOLY
2	A	D	EXILE and BANISH
3	A	F	DUSK and DAWN
4	B	F	GOSSIP and RUMOUR
5	B	E	TEPID and LUKEWARM
6	A	E	CACKLE and CHUCKLE
7	A	D	BULGING and PROTRUDING
8	A	F	SUCCULENT and JUICY
9	B	F	DROP and RELEASE
10	B	E	PLIABLE and FLEXIBLE

Antonyms: Opposite Words
(one word out of three options)

Page 54	Answer	The words most opposite in meaning are...
Example	A	**CONTINUOUS and INTERMITTENT**
1	C	DOUBT and CERTAINTY
2	C	AUDACIOUS and TIMID
3	B	DISINGENUOUS and HONEST
4	A	EXORBITANT and CHEAP
5	C	PROGRESS and REGRESS
6	B	CONCEAL and DIVULGE
7	A	PUTRID and FRESH
8	B	SCARCE and ABUNDANT
9	C	PERMANENT and TEMPORARY
10	A	BOOST and DISCOURAGE

Antonyms: Opposite Words
(one word out of four options)

Page 55	Answer	The words most opposite in meaning are...
Example	B	**PREDICTABLE and UNEXPECTED**
1	C	GREED and MODERATION
2	D	BARREN and FERTILE
3	B	COMPULSORY and VOLUNTARY
4	C	FAULTY and FLAWLESS
5	A	WAX and WANE
6	B	EXPOSED and SHELTERED
7	D	ECONOMICAL and WASTEFUL
8	D	SLACK and TAUT
9	A	IMPROVED and DECLINED
10	D	DETERIORATE and RECOVER

Antonyms: Opposite Words
(one word out of five options)

Page 56	Answer	The words most opposite in meaning are...
Example	E	**IMPROBABLE and LIKELY**
1	E	BLEAK and HOPEFUL
2	B	FEASIBLE and IMPOSSIBLE
3	A	SHAMEFUL and HONOURABLE
4	C	INTEGRATE and SEPARATE
5	E	RUSTIC and URBAN
6	E	DRASTIC and MILD
7	C	STREAMLINED and CUMBERSOME
8	A	ENDORSE and DISAPPROVE
9	D	RATIONAL and ILLOGICAL
10	E	ECLECTIC and RESTRICTED

Antonyms: Opposite Words
(one pair out of four options)

Page 57	Answer	The pair of antonyms is...
Example	C	**VOLUNTARY and OBLIGATORY**
1	C	INDIVIDUAL and COLLECTIVE
2	A	WILD and TAME
3	D	NONCHALENT and FRETFUL
4	C	SUSPECT and TRUSTWORTHY
5	A	TRUANCY and ATTENDANCE
6	B	DISENCHANT and INSPIRE
7	D	ECCENTRIC and ORDINARY
8	B	VOLATILE and STABLE
9	B	SLIGHT and BRAWNY
10	A	JUSTIFIED and UNFAIR

Word Definitions

Page 58	Answer	Choose the best option that offers the best definition of the word on the left.
Example	A	**ARROGANT: closest meaning - a sense of superiority.**
1	B	OSTRACISE: closest meaning - to exclude.
2	A	PALPABLE: closest meaning - able to be felt.
3	C	OBSTINATE: closest meaning - unwilling to change.
4	B	TRAVESTY: closest meaning - a great shame.
5	D	OMIT: closest meaning - to exclude.
6	A	BENEFICIAL: closest meaning - being advantageous.
7	C	PRECLUDE: closest meaning - prevent from occurring.
8	D	OBSOLETE: closest meaning - outdated.
9	B	ABATE: closest meaning - to become less.
10	B	LAMENT: closest meaning - to express sorrow.

Category Fit

Page 59		Select the group that the given word belongs to
Example	**B**	**DIAMOND belongs to the group: stone**
1	C	MANUSCRIPT belongs to the group: text
2	A	FUTON belongs to the group: bedding
3	C	SATCHEL belongs to the group: bag
4	B	ORTHODONTIST belongs to the group: profession
5	C	DODO belongs to the group: animal
6	B	BILLIARDS belongs to the group: game
7	B	THYME belongs to the group: herb
8	C	ODE belongs to the group: poetry
9	D	TENOR belongs to the group: voice
10	C	DECIBEL belongs to the group: sound

BLANK PAGE

BLANK PAGE